BIRD SONGS

BIRD SONGS

COMPILED BY *Gwendolyn Reed*

DRAWINGS BY *Gabriele Margules*

ATHENEUM   *New York   1969*

TO

Sarah Bundy

AND

Ella Mae Simpson

ACKNOWLEDGMENTS

I gratefully acknowledge the permission to reprint the following poems:

"The Birdcage" from *Collected Poems* by Conrad Aiken. Copyright 1953 by Conrad Aiken. Reprinted by permission of Oxford University Press, Inc.

"The Blackbird by Belfast Lough." Reprinted by permission of G. P. Putnam's Sons from *A Short History of Irish Literature* by Frank O'Connor. Copyright © 1967 by Harriet R. O'Donovan.

"The Tiny Bird," "The Tree of Life," "Wrens of the Lake," from *The Irish Tradition* by Robin Flower by permission of The Clarendon Press, Oxford.

"In Praise of May" translated by T. W. Rolleston, from *The High Deeds of Finn* by T. W. Rolleston. By permission of George G. Harrap & Company Limited and Thomas Y. Crowell Company.

"The Yellow Bird" from *The White Pony* by Robert Payne. By permission of Robert Payne.

"The Bird's Epitaph" by Martin Armstrong. Reprinted by permission of A. D. Peters & Co.

"Dawn" from *Poems and Plays* by Gordon Bottomley, The Bodley Head, 1953. By permission of C. Colleen Abbott.

"One Kingfisher and One Yellow Rose" by Eileen Brennan, from *New Irish Poets*. Copyright 1948 by Devin-Adair Company.

"The magpie singing his delight" (from "Bird Cage") from *Speak with the Sun* by David Campbell. By permission of David Campbell and Chatto and Windus Ltd.

"Blue Jay" from *Shoes of the Wind* by Hilda Conkling. Copyright 1922 by J. B. Lippincott Company; copyright renewed 1950 by Hilda Conkling. Published by J. B. Lippincott Company.

"Winter Field" from *Collected Poems* of A. E. Coppard. Copyright 1928 and renewed 1956 by A. E. Coppard. Reprinted by permission of Alfred A. Knopf, Inc. and A. D. Peters & Co.

"O What of the Fowler?" by Charles Dalmon from *Flower and Leaf*. By permission of The Richards Press.

"Jenny Wren," "To Sparrows Fighting." Copyright © 1963 by Jonathan Cape Limited. Reprinted from *The Complete Poems of W. H. Davies* by permission of Mrs. H. M. Davies and Wesleyan University Press.

"A Goldfinch," "Jenny Wren," "A Robin," by Walter de la Mare. By permission of The Literary Trustees of Walter de la Mare and The Society of Authors as their representative.

"Most she touched me by her muteness," "I was a Phoebe." Reprinted by permission of the publishers and the Trustees of Amherst College from Thomas H. Johnson, Editor, *The Poems of Emily Dickinson*, Cambridge, Mass.: The Belknap Press of Harvard University Press, Copyright, 1951, 1955, by The President and Fellows of Harvard College. "Most she touched me by her muteness" from *The Complete Poems of Emily Dickinson* edited by Thomas H. Johnson. Copyright 1929 © 1957 by Mary L. Hampson. Reprinted by permission of Little, Brown & Co.

"Dust of Snow," "Looking for a Sunset Bird in Winter," from *Complete Poems of Robert Frost*. Copyright 1923 by Holt, Rinehart and Winston, Inc. Copyright 1951 by Robert Frost. Reprinted by permission of Holt, Rinehart and Winston, Inc.

"The Swallow" from *The Creatures' Choir* by Carmen Bernos de Gasztold, translated by Rumer Godden. Copyright © 1965 by Rumer Godden. All rights

48991

CONTENTS

Cock Robin

THE ROBIN

The robin is the one
That interrupts the morn
With hurried, few, express reports
When March is scarcely on.

The robin is the one
That overflows the noon
With her cherubic quantity,
And April but begun.

The robin is the one
That speechless from her nest
Submits that home and certainty
And sanctity are best.

Emily Dickinson

ROBIN REDBREAST

(A child's Song)

Good-by, good-by, to Summer:
  For Summer's nearly done;
The garden smiling faintly,
  Cool breezes in the sun;
Our Thrushes now are silent,
  Our Swallows flown away,—
But Robin's here, in coat of brown,
  With ruddy breast-knot gay.
    Robin, Robin Redbreast,
      Oh, Robin dear!
    Robin singing sweetly
      In the falling of the year.

Bright yellow, red, and orange,
  The leaves come down in hosts;
The trees are Indian Princes,
  But soon they'll turn to Ghosts;
The scanty pears and apples
  Hang russet on the bough,
It's Autumn, Autumn, Autumn late,
  'Twill soon be winter now.
    Robin, Robin Redbreast,
      Oh, Robin dear!
    And welaway! my Robin,
      For pinching times are near.

The fireside for the Cricket,
  The wheatstack for the Mouse,
When trembling night-winds whistle
  And moan all round the house;
The frosty ways like iron,

The branches plumed with snow,—
Alas! in Winter, dead and dark,
Where can poor Robin go?
Robin, Robin Redbreast,
Oh, Robin dear!
And a crumb of bread for Robin,
His little heart to cheer.

William Allingham

A ROBIN

Ghost-grey the fall of night,
Ice-bound the lane,
Lone in the dying light
Flits he again;
Lurking where shadows steal,
Perched in his coat of blood,
Man's homestead at his heel,
Death-still the wood.

Odd restless child; it's dark;
All wings are flown
But this one wizard's—hark!—
Stone clapped on stone!
Changeling and solitary,
Secret and sharp and small,
Flits he from tree to tree,
Calling on all.

Walter de la Mare

3

THE RED ROBIN

Cock Robin, he got a new tippet in spring,
And he sat in a shed, and heard other birds sing.
And he whistled a ballad as loud as he could,
And built him a nest of oak leaves by the wood,
And finished it just as the celandine pressed
Like a bright burning blaze, by the edge of its nest,
All glittering with sunshine and beautiful rays,
Like high polished brass, or the fire in a blaze;
Then sung a new song on the edge of the brere;
And so it kept singing the whole of the year.
Till cowslips and wild roses blossomed and died,
The red robin sang by the old spinney side.

John Clare

THE CAT AND THE BIRD

Tell me, tell me, gentle Robin,
What is it sets thy heart a-throbbing?
Is it that Grimalkin fell
Hath killed thy father or thy mother,
Thy sister or thy brother,
Or any other?
Tell me but that,
And I'll kill the Cat.

But stay, little Robin, did you ever spare
A grub on the ground, or a fly in the air?
No, that you never did, I'll swear.
So I won't kill the Cat,
That's flat.

George Canning

4

. . . *And Jenny Wren*

JENNY WREN

Of all the birds that rove and sing,
    Near dwellings made for men,
None is so nimble, feat, and trim
        As Jenny Wren.

With pin-point bill, and a tail a-cock,
    So wildly shrill she cries,
The echoes on his roof-tree knock
        And fill the skies.

Never was sweeter seraph hid
    Within so small a house—
A tiny, inch-long, eager, ardent,
        Feathered mouse.

Walter de la Mare

5

NO COMMUNICATION

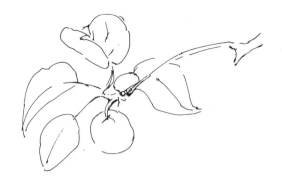

The wren that rages when I sit
Too close to this crabapple tree
Cannot be told, for all her wit,
I hung the gourd she guards from me.

Mark Van Doren

WRENS OF THE LAKE

Wrens of the lake, I love them all,
They come to matins at my call,
The wren whose nest lets through the rain,
He is my goose, my cock, my crane.

My little bard, my man of song
Went on a foray all day long;
Three midges were the poet's prey,
He cannot eat them in a day.

He caught them in his little feet,
His brown claws closed about the meat;
His chicks for dinner gather round,
Sure, if it rains they'll all be drowned.

The crested plover's lost her young,
With bitter grief my heart is stung;
Two little chicks she had—they're gone:
The wren's round dozen still lives on!

TRANSLATED FROM THE IRISH BY
Robin Flower

6

JENNY WREN

Her sight is short, she comes quite near;
A foot to me's a mile to her;
And she is known as Jenny Wren,
The smallest bird in England. When
I heard that little bird at first,
Methought her frame would surely burst
With earnest song. Oft had I seen
Her running under leaves so green,
Or in the grass when fresh and wet,
As though her wings she would forget.
And, seeing this, I said to her—
'My pretty runner, you prefer
To be a thing to run unheard
Through leaves and grass, and not a bird!'
'Twas then she burst, to prove me wrong,
Into a sudden storm of song;
So very loud and earnest, I
Feared she would break her heart and die.
'Nay, nay,' I laughed, 'be you no thing
To run unheard, sweet scold, but sing!
O I could hear your voice near me,
Above the din in that old oak tree,
When almost all the twigs on top
Had starlings chattering without stop.'

W. H. Davies

7

Love's Horn Doth Blow

SONG

A ho! A ho!
Love's horn doth blow,
And he will out a-hawking go.
The sparrows flutter round his wrist,
The feathery thieves that Venus kissed
And taught their morning song,
The linnets seek the airy list,
And swallows too, small pets of spring,
Beat back the gale with swifter wing,
And dart and wheel along.

Thomas Lovell Beddoes

from *The Bride's Tragedy*

8

PACK, CLOUDS, AWAY!

Pack, clouds, away! and welcome, day!
With night we banish sorrow.
Sweet air, blow soft; mount, lark, aloft,
To give my love good-morrow.
Wings from the wind to please her mind,
Notes from the lark I'll borrow:
Bird, prune thy wing, nightingale, sing,
To give my love good-morrow.
   To give my love good-morrow,
   Notes from them all I'll borrow.

Wake from thy nest, robin redbreast,
Sing, birds, in every furrow;
And from each bill let music shrill
Give my fair love good-morrow.
Blackbird and thrush in every bush,
Stare, linnet, and cock-sparrow,
You pretty elves, among yourselves
Sing my fair love good-morrow.
   To give my love good-morrow
   Sing, birds, in every furrow.

Thomas Heywood

9

ANSWER TO A CHILD'S QUESTION

Do you ask what the birds say? The Sparrow, the Dove,
The Linnet and Thrush say, "I love and I love!"
In the winter they're silent—the wind is so strong;
What it says, I don't know, but it sings a loud song.
But green leaves, and blossoms, and sunny warm weather,
And singing, and loving—all come back together.
But the Lark is so brimful of gladness and love,
The green fields below him, the blue sky above,
That he sings, and he sings; and for ever sings he—
"I love my Love, and my Love loves me!"

Samuel Taylor Coleridge

I BEAR, IN SIGN OF LOVE

I bear, in sign of love,
A sparrow in my glove,
And in my breast a dove,
    These shall be all thine;
Besides, of sheep a flock,
Which yieldeth many a lock,
And that shall be thy stock—
    Come, be my valentine!

Francis Andrewes

from *Shepherdess' Valentine*

10

I HAVE FOUND OUT A GIFT FOR MY FAIR

I have found out a gift for my fair;
  I have found where the wood-pigeons breed;
But let me such plunder forbear,
  She will say 'twas a barbarous deed:
For he ne'er could be true, she averr'd,
  Who could rob a poor bird of its young;
And I loved her the more when I heard
  Such tenderness fall from her tongue.

William Shenstone

from *A Pastoral Ballad*

11

Within the Bush

WITHIN THE BUSH

Within the bush her covert nest
A little linnet fondly prest,
The dew sat chilly on her breast,
 Sae early in the morning;
She soon shall see her tender brood,
The pride, the pleasure o' the wood,
Among the fresh green leaves bedew'd
 Awake the early morning.

Robert Burns

from *A Rose-Bud, by my Early Walk*

12

BIRDS' NESTS

And o'er the first bumbarrel's nest
   We wondered at the spell
That birds who served no prenticeship
   Could build their nests so well;
And, finding linnets moss was green,
   And finches choosing grey,
And every finch's nest alike,
   Our wits were all away.

Then blackbirds lining theirs with grass
   And thrushes theirs with dung—
So for our lives we could not tell
   From whence the wisdom sprung.
We marvelled much how little birds
   Should ever be so wise;
And so we guessed some angel came
   To teach them from the skies.

John Clare

from *Childhood*

THE TWO NESTS

The wonder was on me in Curraghmacall,
   When I was as tall as the height of your knee,
That the wren should be building a hole in the wall
   Instead of a nest in a tree.

And I still do be thinking it strange, when I pass
   A pasture that has to be evenly ploughed,
That the lark should be building a hole in the grass
   Instead of a nest in a cloud.

Francis Carlin

13

THE EMPEROR'S BIRD'S-NEST

Once the Emperor Charles of Spain,
  With his swarthy, grave commanders,
I forget in what campaign,
Long besieged, in mud and rain,
  Some old frontier town of Flanders.

Up and down the dreary camp,
  In great boots of Spanish leather,
Striding with a measured tramp,
These Hidalgos, dull and damp,
  Cursed the Frenchmen, cursed the weather.

Thus as to and fro they went
  Over upland and through hollow,
Giving their impatience vent,
Perched upon the Emperor's tent,
  In her nest, they spied a swallow.

Yes, it was a swallow's nest,
  Built of clay and hair of horses,
Mane, or tail, or dragoon's crest,
Found on hedge-rows east and west,
  After skirmish of the forces.

Then an old Hidalgo said,
  As he twirled his gray mustachio,
"Sure this swallow overhead
Thinks the Emperor's tent a shed,
  And the Emperor but a Macho!"

Hearing his imperial name
  Coupled with those words of malice,

14

Half in anger, half in shame,
Forth the great campaigner came
  Slowly from his canvas palace.

"Let no hand the bird molest,"
  Said he solemnly, "nor hurt her!"
Adding then, by way of jest,
"Golondrina is my guest,
  'T is the wife of some deserter!"

Swift as bowstring speeds a shaft,
  Through the camp was spread the rumor,
And the soldiers, as they quaffed
Flemish beer at dinner, laughed
  At the Emperor's pleasant humor.

So unharmed and unafraid
  Sat the swallow still and brooded,
Till the constant cannonade
Through the walls a breach had made,
  And the siege was thus concluded.

Then the army, elsewhere bent,
  Struck its tents as if disbanding,
Only not the Emperor's tent,
For he ordered, ere he went,
  Very curtly, "Leave it standing!"

So it stood there all alone,
  Loosely flapping, torn and tattered,
Till the brood was fledged and flown,
Singing o'er those walls of stone
  Which the cannon-shot had shattered.

Henry Wadsworth Longfellow

15

In the Dark of December

WINTER FIELD

Sorrow on the acres,
  Wind in the thorn,
And an old man ploughing
  Through the frosty morn.

A flock of the dark birds,
  Rooks and their wives,
Follow the plough team
  The old man drives;

And troops of starlings,
  A-tittle-tat and prim,
Follow the rooks
  That follow him.

A. E. Coppard

16

LOOKING FOR A SUNSET BIRD IN WINTER

The west was getting out of gold,
The breath of air had died of cold,
When shoeing home across the white,
I thought I saw a bird alight.

In summer when I passed the place
I had to stop and lift my face;
A bird with an angelic gift
Was singing in it sweet and swift.

No bird was singing in it now.
A single leaf was on a bough,
And that was all there was to see
In going twice around the tree.

From my advantage on a hill
I judged that such a crystal chill
Was only adding frost to snow
As gilt to gold that wouldn't show.

A brush had left a crooked stroke
Of what was either cloud or smoke
From north to south across the blue;
A piercing little star was through.

Robert Frost

17

THAW

Over the land freckled with snow half-thawed
The speculating rooks at their nests cawed
And saw from elm-tops, delicate as flower of grass,
What we below could not see, Winter pass.

Edward Thomas

THE SNOW LIES LIGHT

The snow lies light upon the pine,
The winds are still, the day is fine;
My guests come trooping in to dine.
There are so many to be fed
I have a generous table spread
With corn and nuts and fat and seed
To suit each vagrant's taste and need.

From far and near the jays convene,
And red polls leave the evergreen.
The finch that wears a splendid crown
Is also of the company.
Goldfinches with their gold turned brown,
Juncoes with peeping petticoats,
Tree sparrows lisping whispered notes,
With downy, nuthatch, chickadee,
I welcome to my almonry.

W. W. Christman

from *The Snow Lies Light*

18

WHY CHIDEST THOU THE TARDY SPRING?

Why chidest thou the tardy Spring?
The hardy bunting does not chide;
The blackbirds make the maples ring
With social cheer and jubilee;
The redwing flutes his *o-ka-lee*,
The robins know the melting snow;
The sparrow meek, prophetic-eyed,
Her nest beside the snow-drift weaves,
Secure the osier yet will hide
Her callow brood in mantling leaves,—
And thou, by science all undone,
Why only must thy reason fail
To see the southing of the sun?

Ralph Waldo Emerson

from *May-Day*

BIRDS AT WINTER NIGHTFALL

Around the house the flakes fly faster,
And all the berries now are gone
From holly and cotonea-aster
Around the house. The flakes fly;—faster
Shutting indoors that crumb-outcaster
We used to see upon the lawn
Around the house. The flakes fly faster,
And all the berries now are gone!

Thomas Hardy

19

Summer Is Coming

I KNOW THE TRUSTY ALMANAC

I know the trusty almanac
Of the punctual coming-back,
On their due days, of the birds.
I marked them yestermorn,
A flock of finches darting
Beneath the crystal arch,
Piping, as they flew, a march,—
Belike the one they used in parting
Last year from yon oak or larch;
Dusky sparrows in a crowd,
Diving, darting northward free,
Suddenly betook them all,
Every one to his hole in the wall,
Or to his niche in the apple-tree.

Ralph Waldo Emerson

from *May-Day*

20

SPRING QUIET

Gone were but the Winter,
  Come were but the Spring,
I would go to a covert
  Where the birds sing;

Where in the white-thorn
  Singeth a thrush,
And a robin sings
  In the holly-bush.

Full of fresh scents
  Are the budding boughs,
Arching high over
  A cool green house:

Full of sweet scents,
  And whispering air
Which sayeth softly:
  "We spread no snare;

"Here dwell in safety,
  Here dwell alone,
With a clear stream
  And a mossy stone.

"Here the sun shineth
  Most shadily;
Here is heard an echo
  Of the far sea,
  Though far off it be."

Christina Rossetti

COME, COME AWAY!

Come, come away! the spring,
By every bird that can but sing
Or chirp a note, doth now invite
Us forth to taste of his delight,
In field, in grove, on hill, in dale;
But above all the nightingale,
Who in her sweetness strives t' outdo
The loudness of the hoarse cuckoo.
    "Cuckoo," cries he; "Jug, jug," sings she;
    From bush to bush, from tree to tree:
    Why in one place then tarry we?

Richard Brome

from *The Merry Beggars*

IN PRAISE OF MAY

May-day! delightful day!
Bright colours play the vale along.
Now wakes at morning's slender ray
Wild and gay the blackbird's song.

Now comes the bird of dusty hue,
The loud cuckoo, the summer-lover;
Branchy trees are thick with leaves;
The bitter, evil time is over.

Corncrake sings from eve to morn,
Deep in corn, a strenuous bard!
Sings the virgin waterfall,
White and tall, her one sweet word.

22

Loudly carols the lark on high,
Small and shy, his tireless lay,
Singing in wildest, merriest mood,
Delicate-hued, delightful May.

TRANSLATED FROM THE IRISH BY
T. W. Rolleston

MIDSUMMER

Burnt lawns and iron-bound pastures
    Perplex the feeding thrushes;
All day in the shubbery bushes
    They beat on their anvil stone;
A firm staccato tapping,
    A quick unhurried trapping
    Of many a silly sleepy snail
Who thinks he lives in a coat of mail
And closes his door with a seal of slime—
'Too late, too late, it's feeding time'
Says the busy bird with a beak like a flail,
    As he beats on his anvil stone.
All quiet and cool, the tranquil worm
Lies under the earth so hard and firm,
No probing bird disturbs that crust.
    But overhead in the heat and dust,
    To the four winds the shells are thrown
By the thrush who beats on his anvil stone.

Sybil Horatia Calverley

Cages and Nets

O WHAT IF THE FOWLER?

O what if the fowler my blackbird has taken?
The roses of dawn blossom over the sea;
Awaken, my blackbird, awaken, awaken,
And sing to me out of my red fuchsia tree!

O what if the fowler my blackbird has taken?
The sun lifts his head from the lip of the sea—
Awaken, my blackbird, awaken, awaken,
And sing to me out of my red fuchsia tree!

O what if the fowler my blackbird has taken?
The mountain grows white with the birds of the sea;
But down in my garden, forsaken, forsaken,
I'll weep all the day by my red fuchsia tree.

Charles Dalmon

24

I HAD A DOVE

I had a dove and the sweet dove died,
And I have thought it died of grieving:
O, what could it grieve for? Its feet were tied
With a silken thread of my own hand's weaving;
Sweet little red feet! why should you die—
Why should you leave me, sweet bird! why?
You liv'd alone in the forest-tree,
Why, pretty thing! would you not live with me?
I kiss'd you oft and gave you white peas;
Why not live sweetly, as in the green trees?

John Keats

THE LIBERATOR

In the high trees—many doleful winds:
The ocean waters—lashed into waves.
If the sharp sword be not in your hand,
How can you hope your friends will remain many?
Do you not see that sparrow on the fence?
Seeing the hawk it casts itself into the snare.
The fowler to catch the sparrow is delighted:
The Young Man to see the sparrow is grieved.
He takes his sword and cuts through the netting:
The yellow sparrow flies away, away.
Away, away, up to the blue sky
And down again to thank the Young Man.

Wu-ti, Emperor of the Liang dynasty
TRANSLATED FROM THE CHINESE BY
Arthur Waley

THE BIRDCAGE

The empty birdcage hangs with open door,
shadow of golden wires on golden floor;
Mavis's bird is gone, and Miriam's bird,
like Lesbia's, is a voice no longer heard.

A child remembers, as she thinks, with eyes.
So now, they follow the lost bird where it flies;
lift to the open window, the breadcrumbed sill,
soar to the clouds, remember, and are still;

drop back to an empty cage from empty sky,
flight and return, before they fill and cry;
Mavis and Miriam and Miranda too,
each with a bird, each with a bird that flew.
Molly hangs out an empty cage in moonlight—
luckier, this might be. May, in the sunlight,
purses her lips in a true birdcatcher's whistle.
Moppet sprinkles a leaf with seeds of thistle.

Children think with eyes, first, then with fingers;
both in the eyes and hands the knowledge lingers.
Marian's eyes and fingers suffer much,
remembering now how soft it was to touch.

All through the streets the empty cages hang,
bare little cells, where once the sweet birds sang.
Someone we loved has left this cage, the city.
Someone has left our hearts, and O the pity.

Conrad Aiken

O LAPWING

O Lapwing, thou fliest around the heath,
Nor seest the net that is spread beneath.
Why dost thou not fly among the corn fields?
They cannot spread nets where a harvest yields.

William Blake

LET YE THEN MY BIRDS ALONE

Sure my sparrows are my own,
Let ye then my birds alone.
Come, poor birds! from foes severe
Fearless come, you're welcome here;
My heart yearns at fate like yours,
A sparrow's life's as sweet as ours.
Hardy clowns! grudge not the wheat
Which hunger forces birds to eat:
Your blinded eyes, worst foes to you,
Can't see the good which sparrows do.
Did not poor birds with watching rounds
Pick up the insects from your grounds,
Did they not tend your rising grain.
You then might sow to reap in vain.

John Clare

from *Summer Evening*

27

Children of the Wind

THE WOODPECKER

He walks still upright from the root,
Measuring the timber with his foot,
And all the way, to keep it clean,
Doth from the bark the wood-moths glean;
He, with his beak, examines well
Which fit to stand, and which to fell;
The good he numbers up, and hacks
As if he mark'd them with an axe;
But where he, tinkling with his beak,
Does find the hollow oak to speak,
That for his building he designs,
And through the tainted side he mines.

Andrew Marvell

from *Appleton House*

28

I WAS A PHOEBE

I was a Phoebe—nothing more—
A Phoebe—nothing less—
The little note that others dropt
I fitted into place—

I dwelt too low that any seek—
Too shy, that any blame—
A Phoebe makes a little print
Upon the Floors of Fame—

Emily Dickinson

BLUE JAY

All the flowers are sleeping,
A feather blanket of snow
Over them.
Blue Jay balances on a dry old sun—
    flower's bent head . . .
He dives under . . .
He strikes out seeds with angry
    beak.
His wings are barred with frost,
His snow-dusty feet
Are like dull crystal.
I like him . . . almost . . .
But must he keep on screeching in
    such a voice
And the flowers at their wits' end
For a little quiet?

Hilda Conkling

29

THE TINY BIRD

The tiny bird
Whose call I heard
I marked his yellow bill;
The ousel's glee
Above Lough Lee
Shakes golden branches still.

TRANSLATED FROM THE IRISH BY
Robin Flower

TO SPARROWS FIGHTING

Stop, feathered bullies!
  Peace, angry birds;
You common Sparrows that,
  For a few words,
Roll fighting in wet mud,
To shed each other's blood.

Look at those Linnets, they
  Like ladies sing;
See how those Swallows, too,
  Play on the wing;
All other birds close by
Are gentle, clean and shy.

And yet maybe your life's
  As sweet as theirs;
The common poor that fight
Live not for years
In one long frozen state
Of anger, like the great.

W. H. Davies

30

THE SWALLOW

Who is quick, quick, quick,
and lives, Lord,
if not I?
Small black arrow
of Your blue sky.
I stun the wind
by the swift ease
of my flight
but, under the eaves of the roof,
in their cozy clay home,
my nestlings are hungry.
Quick, quick, quick,
in the hunt for their food,
I dart
from the top to the bottom
of heaven
with a whistle of joy;
then my beak opens
to snap up some inalert fly.
Lord,
a day will come,
a chill gold day
when my babes will take wing
on their own affairs.
Oh! On that day,
when there will be nothing more to bring,
console me
with the call of countries far away.

Amen.

Carmen Bernos de Gasztold
TRANSLATED FROM THE FRENCH BY
Rumer Godden

31

CUCKOO'S PALACE

Oh, the Cuckoo, he is a royal bird,
To have seven queens (which seems absurd)!
One cleans his parlour with mop and broom;
The second one carries the pail from the room;
The third with a napkin wipes his plate;
The fourth brings his bread and his wine in state;
The fifth stands by to plenish his cup,
The sixth she carries the coal-pan up
At night, to make the sheets feel warm;
The seventh she sleeps with her head on his arm.

William Brighty Rands

PIGEON ENGLISH

The plump, the pompous bosomed bird
Perches upon the steepled roof.
He wears a look of mild reproof,
And speaks in accents soft and blurred.
One pessimistic theme is his:
"and the difficulty is . . . . and the difficulty is . . . ."

His neighbor sits and cocks an eye
Upon the crowded street below.
He sees the people come and go,
He feels Time's feathered wing brush by,
Nods his head sagely, and says he:
"Indubitably . . . . indubitably . . . ."

Sara Henderson Hay

32

THE ECHOING CLIFF

White gulls that sit and float
Each on his shadow like a boat,
Sandpipers, oystercatchers
And herons, those grey stilted watchers,
From loch and corran rise,
And as they scream and squawk abuse
Echo from wooded cliff replies
So clearly that the dark pine boughs,
Where goldcrests flit
And owls in drowsy wisdom sit,
Are filled with sea-birds and their cries.

Andrew Young

SEDGE-WARBLERS

And sedge-warblers, clinging so light
To willow twigs, sang longer than the lark,
Quick, shrill, or grating, a song to match the heat
Of the strong sun, nor less the water's cool,
Gushing through narrows, swirling in the pool.
Their song that lacks all words, all melody,
All sweetness almost, was dearer then to me
Than sweetest voice that sings in tune sweet words.
This was the best of May—the small brown birds
Wisely reiterating endlessly
What no man learnt yet, in or out of school.

Edward Thomas

from *Sedge-Warblers*

33

THE MAGPIE SINGING HIS DELIGHT

The magpie singing his delight
An unskilled artisan may be;
In dinner suit of black and white
He only gets the sun for fee;
Yet sweetly still his notes will come
When all our instruments are dumb.

David Campbell

from *Bird Cage*

THE HERON

The heron stands in water where the swamp
Has deepened to the blackness of a pool,
Or balances with one leg on a hump
Of marsh grass heaped above a muskrat hole.

He walks the shallow with an antic grace.
The great feet break the ridges of the sand,
The long eye notes the minnow's hiding place.
His beak is quicker than a human hand.

He jerks a frog across his bony lip,
Then points his heavy bill above the wood.
The wide wings flap but once to lift him up.
A single ripple starts from where he stood.

Theodore Roethke

CUCKOO IN THE PEAR-TREE

The Cuckoo sat in the old pear-tree.

        Cuckoo!

Raining or snowing, naught cared he.

        Cuckoo!

    Cuckoo, cuckoo, naught cared he.
The Cuckoo flew over a housetop nigh.

        Cuckoo!

"Dear, are you at home, for here am I?

        Cuckoo!

    Cuckoo, cuckoo, here am I."
"I dare not open the door to you.

        Cuckoo!

Perhaps you are not the right cuckoo?

        Cuckoo!

    Cuckoo, cuckoo, the right Cuckoo!"
"I am the right Cuckoo, the proper one.

        Cuckoo!

For I am my father's only son,

        Cuckoo!

    Cuckoo, cuckoo, his only son."
"If you are your father's only son—

        Cuckoo!

    The bobin pull tightly,
    Come through the door lightly—

        Cuckoo!

    If you are our father's only son—

        Cuckoo!

It must be you, the only one—
    Cuckoo, cuckoo, my own Cuckoo!

        Cuckoo!

William Brighty Rands

35

THE CARDINAL

Cardinal, lover of shade . . .
Rock and gold is the land in the pulsing noon.
Lover of cedar, lover of shade . . .
Blue is the shadow of cedar on grey limestone,
Where the lizard, devout as an ikon,
Is carved on the stone, throat pulsing on lichen.

At the hour of noon I have seen
The burst of your wings displayed,
Vision of scarlet devised in the slumberous green
. . . Lover of cedar and shade.

What if the lizard, my cardinal,
Depart like a breath from its altar, summer southward fail?
Here is a bough where you can perch, and preen
Your scarlet that from its landscape shall not fade,
Lapped in the cool of the mind's undated shade,
In a whispering tree, like cedar, evergreen.

Robert Penn Warren

THE DOVE

I once in happy times
Within my leafy grove,
With joyful voice did rove
And with the cuckoo sing
And now am like a dove
That in his grief alone
Upon some beam may moan
The losing of a wing.

William Barnes

36

THE MISSEL-THRUSH

That missel-thrush
Scorns to alight on a low bush,
And as he flies
And tree-top after tree-top tries,
His shadow flits
And harmlessly on tree-trunk hits.

Shutting his wings
He sways and sings and sways and sings,
And from his bough
As in deep water he looks through
He sees me there
Crawl at the bottom of the air.

Andrew Young

SANDPIPERS

Ten miles of flat land along the sea.
Sandland where the salt water kills the sweet potatoes.
Homes for sandpipers—the script of their feet is on the sea shingles—
    they write in the morning, it is gone at noon—they write at
    noon, it is gone at night.
Pity the land, the sea, the ten mile flats, pity anything but the sand-
    pipers' wire legs and feet.

Carl Sandburg

37

THE BLACKBIRD BY BELFAST LOUGH

What little throat
Has framed that note?
What gold beak shot
   It far away?
A blackbird on
His leafy throne
Tossed it alone
   Across the bay.

TRANSLATED FROM THE IRISH BY
Frank O'Connor

A GOLDFINCH

This feather-soft creature
Is, tail to head,
A golden yellow,
And black, and red.

A sip of water,
A twig to sing on,
A prong for nest,
The air to wing on,

A mate to love,
Some thistledown seed
Are all his joy, life,
Beauty, need.

Walter de la Mare

38

THE CHILD AND THE SPARROW

CHILD.   Sparrow, in the cherry-tree,
          Won't you drop one down for me?

SPARROW.   Presently, presently.

CHILD.   Sparrow, Sparrow, greedy-pate,
          There's a fine one! drop it straight!

SPARROW.   Little boys should learn to wait.

CHILD.   Sparrow, without more ado,
          Come, be kind, and drop me two.

SPARROW.   They're not ripe enough for you.

CHILD.   Saucy, Sparrow, cease your fun!
          What! you're off, and give me none!

SPARROW.   All are gone, all are gone!

Thomas Westwood

39

Listening . . . Watching

DAWN

A thrush is tapping a stone
With a snail-shell in its beak;
A small bird hangs from a cherry
Until the stem shall break.
No waking song has begun,
And yet birds chatter and hurry
And throng in the elm's gloom
Because an owl goes home.

Gordon Bottomley

40

ONE KINGFISHER AND
ONE YELLOW ROSE

Taking pity on this scrag-end of the city
Is my one kingfisher
Sitting stiffly on his willow
And staring at my one yellow rose.
I like him for his blueness
And more so for his kindness,
But I wish I had a garden
Then I wouldn't be depending
On this one kingfisher
And on one yellow rose.

There's a man, says one who knows,
Who is always in a hurry—
His mind's on making money
For a garden
Where he harbours
Many a kingly fisher
And many a quality rose.
But he's not the man he was,
Says my one who knows,
Since his fellows stopped saluting him
With: How's your one kingfisher?
And: How's that yellow rose?

Eileen Brennan

THE BLIND MAN

Speak of the birds, he lifts a listening finger
And 'chiff-chaff' 'willow-warbler' names each singer,
'Hedge-sparrow' 'robin' 'wren'; he knows their cries,
Though all are nightingales to his blind eyes.

Andrew Young

41

IN GLENCULLEN

Thrush, linnet, stare, and wren,
Brown lark beside the sun,
Take thought of kestrel, sparrow-hawk,
Birdlime and roving gun.

You great-great-grandchildren
Of birds I've listened to,
I think I robbed your ancestors
When I was young as you.

John M. Synge

MOST SHE TOUCHED ME BY HER MUTENESS

Most she touched me by her muteness—
Most she won me by the way
She presented her small figure—
Plea itself—for Charity—
Were a Crumb my whole possession—
Were there famine in the land—
Were it my resource from starving—
Could I such a plea withstand—

Not upon her knee to thank me
Sank this beggar from the Sky—
But the Crumb partook—departed—
And returned On High—

I supposed—when sudden
Such a Praise began
'Twas a Space sat singing
To herself—and men—

42

'Twas the Winged Beggar—
Afterward I learned
To her Benefactor
Making Gratitude

Emily Dickinson

THE RIVALS

I heard a bird at dawn
Singing sweetly on a tree,
That the dew was on the lawn,
And the wind was on the lea;
But I didn't listen to him,
For he didn't sing to me!

I didn't listen to him,
For he didn't sing to me
That the dew was on the lawn,
And the wind was on the lea!
I was singing at the time,
Just as prettily as he!

I was singing all the time,
Just as prettily as he,
About the dew upon the lawn,
And the wind upon the lea!
So I didn't listen to him,
As he sang upon a tree!

James Stephens

THE YELLOW BIRD

O yellow bird, yellow bird,
Do not settle on the poppy,
Do not peck my millet seed,
For the people here
Do not want me to feed.
I must go back, I must go home
To my own people, my own land.

O yellow bird, yellow bird,
Do not settle on the mulberry,
Do not peck my maize seed.
With the people of this land
There can be no covenant.
I must go back, I must go home
To where my brothers are.

O yellow bird, yellow bird,
Do not settle on the oak,
Do not peck my wine millet.
With the people here
I cannot dwell.
I must go back, I must go home
To my own folks.

TRANSLATED FROM THE CHINESE BY
Robert Payne

44

Te Whit, Te Whoo

THE BIRD OF NIGHT

A shadow is floating through the moonlight.
Its wings don't make a sound.
Its claws are long, its beak is bright.
Its eyes try all the corners of the night.

It calls and calls: all the air swells and heaves
And washes up and down like water.
The ear that listens to the owl believes
In death. The bat beneath the eaves,
The mouse beside the stone are still as death.
The owl's air washes them like water.
The owl goes back and forth inside the night,
And the night holds its breath.

Randall Jarrell

45

THE BONNY, BONNY OWL

The lark is but a bumpkin fowl,
    He sleeps in his nest till morn;
But my blessings upon the jolly owl,
    That all night blows his horn.
Then up with your cup till you stagger in speech,
And match me this catch though you swagger and screech,
And drink till you wink, my merry men each;
For though hours be late, and weather be foul,
We'll drink to the health of the bonny, bonny owl.

Sir Walter Scott

from *Kenilworth*

THEN FROM A RUIN

Then from a Ruin where conceal'd he lay
Watching his buried Gold, and hating Day,
Hooted *The Owl.*—"I tell you, my Delight
Is in the Ruin and the Dead of Night
Where I was born, and where I love to wone
All my Life long, sitting on some cold stone
Away from all your roystering Companies,
In some dark Corner where a Treasure lies,
That, buried by some Miser in the Dark,
Speaks up to me at Midnight like a Spark;
And o'er it like a Talisman I brood,
Companion of the Serpent and the Toad.

Farid-uddin Attar
TRANSLATED FROM THE PERSIAN BY
Edward FitzGerald

46

THE OWL

Downhill I came, hungry, and yet not starved;
Cold, yet had heat within me that was proof
Against the North wind; tired, yet so that rest
Had seemed the sweetest thing under a roof.

Then at the inn I had food, fire, and rest,
Knowing how hungry, cold, and tired was I.
All of the night was quite barred out except
An owl's cry, a most melancholy cry

Shaken out long and clear upon the hill,
No merry note, nor cause of merriment,
But one telling me plain what I escaped
And others could not, that night, as in I went.

And salted was my food, and my repose,
Salted and sobered, too, by the bird's voice
Speaking for all who lay under the stars,
Soldiers and poor, unable to rejoice.

Edward Thomas

47

Hark, Hark, the Lark

ADDRESS TO A LARK SINGING IN WINTER

Ay, little larky! what's the reason,
Singing thus in winter season?
Nothing, surely, can be pleasing
    To make thee sing;
For I see naught but cold and freezing,
    And feel its sting.

Let mine, sweet bird, then be a warning:
Advice, in season, don't be scorning;
But wait till spring's first days are dawning
    To glad and cheer thee;
And then, sweet minstrel of the morning,
    I'd wish to hear thee.

John Clare

from *Address to a Lark*

48

WHO IS'T NOW WE HEAR?

"Who is't now we hear?
None but the lark so shrill and clear;
Now at heaven's gate she claps her wings,
The morn not waking till she sings."

John Lyly

from *Alexander and Campaspe*

AS I WAS A-WALKING

As I was a-walking
One morning in spring,
I heard a pretty ploughboy,
And so sweetly he did sing:
And as he was a-singing O
These words I heard him say:
'There's no life like the ploughboy's
In the sweet month of May.'

There's the lark in the morning
She will rise up from her nest,
And she'll mount the white air
With the dew on all her breast,
And with this pretty ploughboy O,
She'll whistle and she'll sain,
And at night she'll return
To her nest again.

Anonymous

49

Caw, Caw, Caw

THE CROW

Thou dusky spirit of the wood,
Bird of an ancient brood,
Flitting thy lonely way,
A meteor in the summer's day,
From wood to wood, from hill to hill,
Low over forest, field and rill,
What wouldst thou say?
Why shouldst thou haunt the day?
What makes thy melancholy float?
What bravery inspires thy throat,
And bears thee up above the clouds,
Over desponding human crowds,
Which far below
Lay thy haunts low?

Henry Thoreau

50

ALWAYS WITH US!—
THE BLACK PREACHER

Betimes a wise guest
His visit will sever,
Yes, absence endears.
Revisit he would,
So remains not forever.

Well, Robin the wise one
He went yestreen,
Bound for the South
Where his chums convene.

Back, he'll come back
In his new Spring vest
And the more for his absence
Be welcomed with zest.

But thou, black Crow,
Inconsiderate fowl,
Wilt never away—
Take elsewhere thy cowl?

From the blasted hemlock's
Whitened spur
Whatever the season,
Or Winter or Ver
Or Summer or Fall,
Croaker, foreboader,
We hear thy call—
Caw! Caw! Caw!

Herman Melville

NIGHT CROW

When I saw that clumsy crow
Flap from a wasted tree,
A shape in the mind rose up:
Over the gulfs of dream
Flew a tremendous bird
Further and further away
Into a moonless black,
Deep in the brain, far back.

Theodore Roethke

DUST OF SNOW

The way a crow
Shook down on me
The dust of snow
From a hemlock tree

Has given my heart
A change of mood
And saved some part
Of a day I had rued.

Robert Frost

52

Silence and Songs

SILENCE

Under a low sky—
this quiet morning
of red and
yellow leaves—

a bird disturbs
no more than one twig
of the green leaved
peach tree

William Carlos Williams

SMALL BIRDS

Small birds who sweep into a tree
—A storm of fluttering, stilled as suddenly,
Making the light slip round a shaken berry,
Swinging slim sunlight twigs uncertainly,
Are moved by ripples of light discontent
—Quick waves of anger, breaking through the tree
And tart as sloe-berry.

Peter Quennell

THE MAKING OF BIRDS

God made Him birds in a pleasant humour;
  Tired of planets and suns was He.
He said: 'I will add a glory to Summer,
  Gifts for my creatures banished from me!'

He had a thought and it set Him smiling
  Of the shape of a bird and its glancing head,
Its dainty air and its grace beguiling:
  'I will make feathers,' the Lord God said.

He made the robin; He made the swallow;
  His deft hands moulding the shape to His mood,
The thrush and lark and the finch to follow,
  And laughed to see that His work was good.

He Who has given men gift of laughter—
  Made in His image; He fashioned fit
The blink of the owl and the stork thereafter,
  The little wren and the long-tailed tit.

54

He spent in the making His wit and fancies;
   The wing-feathers He fashioned them strong;
Deft and dear as daisies and pansies,
   He crowned His work with the gift of song.

Dearlings, He said, make songs for My praises!
   He tossed them loose to the sun and wind,
Airily sweet as pansies and daisies;
   He taught them to build a nest to their mind.

The dear Lord God of His glories weary—
   Christ our Lord had the heart of a boy—
Made Him birds in a moment merry,
   Bade them soar and sing for His joy.

Katherine Tynan

A BIRD'S EPITAPH

Here lies a little bird.
   Once all day long
Through Martha's house was heard
   His rippling song.

Tread lightly where he lies
   Beneath this stone
With nerveless wings, closed eyes,
   And sweet voice gone.

Martin Armstrong

55

SING IN THE SILENT SKY

Sing in the silent sky,
  Glad soaring bird;
Sing out thy notes on high
To sunbeam straying by
Or passing cloud;
  Heedless if thou art heard
Sing thy full song aloud.

Christina Rossetti

from *A Summer Wish*

A DEAD BIRD

Finding the feathers of a bird
Killed by a sparrow-hawk,
I thought, What need is there to walk?
And bound them on my feet;
And as I flew off through the air,
I saw men stare up from a street
And women clasp their hands in prayer.
'To Hades' was no sooner said
Than a winged Hermes I was there;
And though I peered round for the dead,
Nothing I saw and nothing heard
But a low moaning from a bough,
'Ah, who is wearing my poor feathers now?'

Andrew Young

56

THESE CHILDREN OF THE WIND

On the shores of Lake Michigan
high on a wooden pole, in a box,
two purple martins had a home
and taken away down to Martinique
and let loose, they flew home,
thousands of miles to be home again.
    And this has lights of wonder
    echo and pace and echo again.
The birds let out began flying
north north-by-west north
till they were back home.
How their instruments told them
of ceiling, temperature, air pressure,
how their control-boards gave them
reports of fuel, ignition, speeds,
is out of the record, out.
    Across spaces of sun and cloud,
in rain and fog, through air pockets,
wind with them, wind against them,
stopping for subsistence rations,
whirling in gust and spiral,
these people of the air,
these children of the wind,
had a sense of where to go and how,
how to go north north-by-west north,
till they came to one wooden pole,
till they were home again.
    And this has lights of wonder
    echo and pace and echo again
for other children, other people, yes.

Carl Sandburg

from *The People, Yes*

57

THE TREE OF LIFE

The Tree of Life with bloom unchanged,
Round it the goodly hosts are ranged,
Its leafy crest showers dewdrops round
All Heaven's spreading garden-ground.

There flock bright birds, a shining throng,
And sing their grace-perfected song
While boundless mercy round them weaves
Undying fruit, unfading leaves.

A lovely flock! bright like the sun,
A hundred feathers clothe each one,
And pure and clear they chant together
A hundred songs for every feather.

TRANSLATED FROM THE IRISH BY
Robin Flower

58

AUTHOR-TITLE INDEX

59